Discovery
CHANNEL

DIVE INTO
SHARKS

UP CLOSE AND PERSONAL

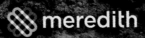
meredith

Thea Feldman, Editor and Writer
Matthew Eberhart, Designer
Andy Dehart, Consulting Editor
Terri Fredrickson, Copyeditor
Kari Greenfield, Licensing Manager

Waterbury Publications, Inc.
Ken Carlson, Creative Director
Doug Samuelson, Associate Design Director

DISCOVERY
CHANNEL ™

meredith

Photography Credits: 3 Jaqui Martin | Dreamstime; 4, 5 Willtu | Dreamstime; 6, 7 Louise Roach | Dreamstime; 8, 9 Jason Hindman | Dreamstime, lukyslukys | Dreamstime; 10,11 Bobby Deal | Dreamstime, John Casey | Dreamstime; 12,13 Oleg Osipov | Dreamstime; 14, 15 photomyeye | Dreamstime, Nicola Vernizzi | Dreamstime; 16, 17 Nathan Ciurzynski | Dreamstime; 17 Gwen Lowe | SeaPics.com; 20, 21 Ami Levin | Dreamstime; 21 Tsuneo Nakamura | SeaPics.com; 22, 23 Onaia | Dreamstime; Luis Louro | Dreamstime;24, 25 Timothy Lubcke | Dreamstime; 26, 27 Naluphoto | Dreamstime, Mark Doherty | Dreamstime; 28, 29 Harold Bolten | Dreamstime, Ian Scott | Dreamstime; 30, 31 Metering | Dreamstime; 30, 31 Norbert Wu and Flip Nicklin | Minden Pictures; 32, 33 Dennis Sabo | Dreamstime; 32 Hirose | e-Photography | SeaPics.com; 34 Amos Nachoum | SeaPics.com; 35 Richard Herrmann | Minden Pictures; 36, 37 Carol Buchanan | Dreamstime, Naluphoto | Dreamstime, Patryk Kosmider | Dreamstime, Ian Scott | Dreamstime, Willtu | Dreamstime; 38, 39 Kevin Panizza | Dreamstime; 40, 41 Dirk-Jan Mattaar | Dreamstime; 42, 43 Chezzzl | Dreamstime; 43 Gwen Lowe | SeaPics.com; 44, 45 Michael Wood | Dreamstime, Alex Edmonds | Dreamstime; 46,47 Paul Banter | Dreamstime, stephankerkhofs | Dreamstime; 48 J. Henning Buchholz.

Table of Contents

Sharks: Up Close and Personal

SHARKS. THE VERY WORD FASCINATES AND MAKES THE SPINE TINGLE.

But while there is an apparently endless curiosity about these predatory swimmers, it's not so easy to find out about them. Any creature that lives in the sea, often where it is deep and dark, is hard to study.

That's, in part, why studying sharks is exciting for marine biologists: as technology develops, there's always something new to discover about shark behavior and habitats. And Discovery Channel has their own killer formula for bringing the most fascinating, fun, and up-to-date shark information to television audiences each summer. Since 1988 it has aired a weeklong series of programs called Shark Week. Shark experts team up with specially trained filmographers who make their way down to the deep sea. Armed with little more than waterproof equipment, the crew captures sharks "at home."

SHARK WEEK
Discovery Channel surprised those passing by their headquarters during Shark Week with a super-sized shark.

With an animal as intriguing as the shark, there has been no shortage of topics to cover. Over the years, shows have focused on extremely rare sharks, killer sharks, prehistoric sharks, shark conservation efforts, and more. Celebrity hosts often narrate the shows, but there's no doubt that the real superstars are the sharks themselves, brought into *our* homes—up close and personal.

Sharks Species Have Seniority

THE MOST FEARSOME FISH IN THE SEA, SHARKS ARE AMONG THE WORLD'S OLDEST LIFE FORMS.

Ancestors of today's sharks first appeared between 420 and 455 million years ago.

How long ago is that? Well, consider this. Sharks appeared about 200 million years *before* the first dinosaurs plodded their way across the planet! Sharks lived in a world that had not yet seen the likes of insects, amphibians, reptiles, or even flowers. People didn't make an appearance until sharks had been around for about 419 million years!

Scientists study **fossils**, remains from ancient sharks, to determine what the forerunners of today's sharks were like. They've found some basic similarities and a lot of fascinating differences. For instance, the lower jaw of *Helicoprion,* a shark from 250 million years ago, was covered with sawlike teeth that curled in a spiral beneath the shark's head! Other sharks had double- or triple-fanged teeth.

THE EVOLUTION OF SHARKS

455 MILLION YEARS AGO
Jawed sharks evolve

435 MILLION YEARS AGO
First bony fish and first land plants and animals appear

408 MILLION YEARS AGO
First insects and amphibians appear

360 MILLION YEARS AGO
First reptiles appear

SHARK NOTE

The largest known shark species today is the Whale Shark. Turn to page 40 to get the BIG news about this shark superstar!

Megaladon is believed to be the largest shark species ever. **Fossil** records have led scientists to estimate that, on average, these whoppers of the water weighed about 50 tons and were 60 feet long. Their impressive dentistry included teeth that could be 6.5 inches long!

Megaladon appeared 16 million years ago, and then died out about 1.6 million years ago. No shark swimming today matches this long-ago sea giant's size and mass.

SHARK BITE!

THE MODERN SHARK AND EXTENDED FAMILY

Scientists estimate there are at least 400 different species of sharks in the world today. Many researchers believe there are shark species yet to be discovered, since it is difficult to find and study animals that live in deep waters, especially when those animals might bite back!

Skates and rays are believed to have evolved from sharks. There are roughly 500 or so species of these shark relatives swimming in the same waters where sharks are found.

250 MILLION YEARS AGO	208 MILLION YEARS AGO	145 MILLION YEARS AGO	25 MILLION YEARS TO 2 MILLION YEARS AGO
Helicoprion swims in the oceans; early dinosaurs, mammals, and marine reptiles appear	First modern sharks and rays appear	Sandtiger shark swims in the oceans; Tyrannosaurus was hunting on land	Megaladon swims in the oceans

No Bones About Shark Anatomy

SHARKS HAVE SURVIVED AND THRIVED FOR SO LONG, THANKS IN PART TO SOME UNIQUE BODY FEATURES AND FUNCTIONS.

Most fish have hard, bony skeletons, but not sharks (or skates or rays). A shark skeleton is made of **cartilage**, a tough but flexible material like that found in human ears.

Cartilage is lighter than bone, so it helps a shark weigh less in the water. It also allows a shark to move and maneuver swiftly through ocean currents, helping it effectively hunt prey.

Bony fish have large scales on their skin. Sharks have small, almost toothlike scales called **dermal denticles**. Dermal denticles not only protect a shark's body, but they can also channel the way water flows over the shark in

SHARK BITE!

CAVE OF THE SLEEPING SHARKS

In the 1970s, scientists investigated several underwater caves in the waters off Isla Mujeres, Mexico. They found a surprising sight—Caribbean Reef Sharks, which breath only by ram ventilation and therefore usually need to keep moving, were found floating motionless inside. The sharks' eyes were open, so they weren't asleep, just clearly resting. Scientists determined that the water inside the cave was higher in oxygen and lower in salt than the water outside the cave, and that this allowed the sharks to take a "time out." This place is now known as the Cave of the Sleeping Sharks.

order to help it move forward quickly.

Like all fish, sharks breathe through gills, which filter oxygen out of the water. Some sharks have a set of muscles called a **gill pump** that sucks in water and pushes it past the gills. Because a gill pump is on the job, working sort of like human lungs, a shark can take in oxygen without moving.

Most sharks also pass water over their gills when they move forward in the water. A shark has at least five gill slits on each side of its body behind its head. When a shark gets oxygen this way, it is using **ram ventilation.**

Some sharks only get oxygen using the ram ventilation method. These are high-energy fish—they keep moving so they don't suffocate and drown!

SHARK NOTE

About two dozen kinds of sharks breathe only using ram ventilation, including the Great White Shark, Mako Shark, and Whale Shark.

Moving Right Along

A SHARK'S TORPEDO-SHAPE BODY GLIDES SMOOTHLY THROUGH THE WATER, ABLY AIDED BY ITS FINS.

Did you know that most sharks have five different kinds of fins?

The fins, which mostly come in pairs, perform a variety of different functions. The **dorsal fin**, located on a shark's back, is the fish's most notorious body part. This is the part swimmers are usually keeping an eye out for on the surface of the water. But the dorsal fin's function is to stabilize the shark as it moves through the water. Some sharks have a second, smaller dorsal fin, located farther down the back.

No one can ever accuse a shark of being unstable because it also has **pelvic fins** to help keep it balanced. In addition, many sharks have **anal fins** to help with stabilization as well.

Nostrils

Snout

Eye

Gills

Mouth

Pectoral fin

SHARK BITE!

KEEPING THINGS LIGHT

A swim bladder not only helps bony fish move up and down in the water, but it also helps keep them buoyant. So how do sharks manage to stay afloat since they lack this organ? Cartilage is lighter than bone, which helps keep a shark light. And a shark has a liver filled with oil that provides some buoyancy. But the only way sharks can keep from sinking, is to swim. The only exception to this is the Sandtiger shark that gulps air into its stomach for buoyancy.

A shark swishes its tail fin (also known as the **caudal fin**) back and forth through the water to propel it forward. Tail fin shapes vary depending on the kind of shark, but many tail fins are fork shaped, with the upper part being larger than the lower part.

Pectoral fins, located on the side of the body, help the shark move up and down in the water. When a shark tilts its pectoral fins up, the water pressure beneath the fins pushes the shark up. When a shark tilts its pectoral fins down, the water pressure on top of the fins pushes the shark deeper in the water.

Upper lobe of caudal fin

Dorsal fin

Dorsal fin*

Lower lobe of caudal fin

Anal fin*

Not found on all sharks

Pectoral fin

Pelvic (or ventral) fin

SHARK NOTE

A shark can easily move forward, up, and down in the water, but unlike other fish it can't swim backward or stop suddenly. It seems it can't shift into reverse and lacks breaks!

A Strong Sense of Things

SHARKS HAVE AN IMPRESSIVE ARRAY OF SENSES THAT HELP THEM NAVIGATE THEIR WAY THROUGH DEEP, DARK, AND OFTEN MURKY WATER.

Most sharks have an excellent sense of sight. With eyes on either side of their heads, sharks also have a very wide field of vision.

Sharks can also hear low-pitch sounds, called **infrasounds**, well below the range of human hearing. Even in the dense water, they can hear the sounds of fish in trouble, splashing swimmers, and boat engines.

A shark's nose is a finely honed smelling machine. A shark can tell which way to go to find prey because smells enter either its left or right nostril first! Sharks like the Great White Shark are legendary for smelling one drop of blood in the water over a mile away.

A shark's taste buds line its entire mouth and are not on its tongue. Sharks can be picky eaters—if they don't like the way something tastes, they'll spit it out! Scientists believe that sharks really don't crave human flesh, and once they get a taste of it, they usually move on, looking for something more satisfying.

SHARK NOTE

A shark's vision is best at a distance. Things close up tend to look blurry, and it's believed that many a shark has accidentally chomped on the wrong thing—like a person it mistakes for a seal or sea lion!

When it comes to feeling things, a shark can use its **lateral line** to sense the vibrations of other things moving in the water. The lateral line is a set of tubes beneath the shark's skin that runs down the fish's head and body.

Perhaps the most amazing sensory part of a shark is the **ampullae of Lorenzini.** These receptor cells under the skin in a shark's head allow it to pick up low levels of electrical energy emitted by animals around it!

SHARK BITE!

ON THE MENU

A shark's sharp senses undoubtedly help it locate food. As for what exactly a shark eats, no matter what lives in the water, it's probably food for some kind of shark. All sharks are **carnivores**, or meat eaters. Most eat fish, squid, and **crustaceans**, such as crabs and lobsters. Some eat sea turtles, while others eat marine mammals like sea lions and seals.

Looking Sharp

A SHARK'S TEETH ARE ITS MOST OBVIOUS AND IMPRESSIVE ASSET.

A single shark can have hundreds of teeth in its mouth at one time, all ready for eating action.

Different kinds of sharks have different kinds of teeth. Some sharks have long, thin, pointy teeth, perfect for spearing small fish, which the shark will then swallow whole. Still, other sharks have triangular-shape **serrated** teeth that work like hunting knives—they easily cut through flesh and saw through bone. Some sharks have both kinds of teeth,

with thin bottom teeth holding prey in place, while serrated top teeth do their stuff. Yet other sharks have flat, grinding teeth that help when the meal of the day is inside a shell that needs to be cracked open.

A shark uses and then loses its teeth throughout the course of its lifetime. It will either grow new teeth to replace the lost ones, or it might already have several rows of teeth in place. For these sharks, it's like a vending machine: a new tooth moves forward when the tooth in front falls out.

Unlike with humans, it's not a big deal when a shark loses a tooth. Shark teeth

SHARK NOTE

Many people think that no other animal can bite harder than a shark. But pound for pound, scientists believe the title of World's Strongest Bite might rightfully belong to the alligator.

don't have roots and are only connected to the jaw's soft cartilage. It's a routine thing for a tooth to come loose.

A shark's jaw also performs a neat trick. Most animals can only move their lower jaw. But a shark can detach its upper jaw, which allows it to thrust its whole mouth forward to grab its meal.

SHARK BITE!

THE SHARK TOOTH CAPITAL OF THE WORLD

Venice, Florida, located on the Gulf of Mexico, is apparently the place to be if you're looking to build your personal shark tooth collection. Sharks have been swimming in the waters off the Gulf Coast for millions of years, and fossils as well as recent teeth wash up on shore with regularity. This self-proclaimed Shark Tooth Capital of the World holds a shark tooth festival every spring, complete with food, music, arts, crafts, and plenty of shark teeth on display and for sale.

Cookiecutter Shark

Isistius brasiliensis

DON'T LET THIS SHARK'S SMALL SIZE AND CUTE NAME FOOL YOU.

The Cookiecutter Shark is one fierce predator that has a unique feeding style.

During the day the shark swims to the surface, where it emits a greenish glow that helps it blend in with the sunlit water. Just one brown patch on its neck doesn't glow, and that patch apparently looks like the silhouette of a small fish. When a larger predator approaches thinking it's getting a quick meal, the Cookiecutter Shark springs into action.

This shark uses its mouth like a suction cup to attach itself to the side of the larger predator. It grabs onto the flesh with its teeth and rotates its body, tugging until a circle of flesh comes loose. Then the Cookiecutter Shark swims off to have its meal, leaving a cookiecutter hole in the side of an unfortunate tuna, dolphin, whale, or even another shark. The wound isn't big enough to be fatal, but it does leave a lasting scar on the offended party.

FAST FACTS

LENGTH: up to 20 inches
DISTRIBUTION: Pacific, Atlantic, and Indian Oceans
OCEAN DEPTHS: 11,500 feet

CHEW ON THIS!

The Cookiecutter Shark sheds an entire row of teeth at a time, which comes out of its mouth like dentures. Then the shark swallows them! Apparently, it needs the extra calcium supplied by the teeth.

Megamouth
Megachasma pelagios

SIZABLE, YET SECRETIVE, NOT MUCH IS KNOWN ABOUT THIS DEEPWATER FISH THAT WAS FIRST DISCOVERED IN 1976.

So few Megamouths have been reported that each one is given a number. (You'll learn about Megamouth 41 on page 29.) Some scientists think that down deep there's a whole world of Megamouths that have yet to be discovered. Whether or not this is true, most of what scientists have learned about them is from observing dead fish that have surfaced.

The most obvious thing about this fish is that it is appropriately named. Megamouth means "big mouth" and this shark's jaw is so large it extends farther back than its eyes. When the Megamouth opens those jaws, it reveals 50 rows of teeth!

The odd thing is that the shark mostly doesn't use them. Instead, the Megamouth filters in small fish and **plankton**, which is yet another odd thing. Plankton is most abundant near the water's surface, so exactly how this big shark is getting enough of the tiny food it needs by hanging down deep remains a mystery.

CHEW ON THIS!

Some scientists believed that the Megamouth Shark has light-producing organs around its mouth that light up like a neon sign to attract food. While this could explain how the big fish manages to get enough food, it hasn't been proven to be true.

FAST FACTS

LENGTH: up to 17 feet

WEIGHT: up to 1,500 pounds

DISTRIBUTION: Hawaii, California, Philippines, Japan, Australia, Indonesia, Taiwan, Brazil, South Africa, Senegal, Indian Ocean, and Ecuador

OCEAN DEPTHS: 3,000 feet

Japanese Sawshark

Pristiophorus japonicus

THERE'S NO POINT PRETENDING YOU'RE NOT STARING AT THE SNOUT ON THIS FISH.

Lined on both sides with teethlike cutters, the Japanese Sawshark's snout looks like a cross between a power tool and a powerful weapon; and it functions that way too!

The Japanese Sawshark hangs out near the sea floor and uses its snout to dig out prey hiding in the rocks and mud. This flat-headed fish has two **barbels**, or feelers, that hang down on either side of its sawlike snout. The barbels help the Japanese Sawshark detect where prey is hiding, and then the snout swings in action, moving like a saw to uncover a meal. The sawshark's mouth is located below its snout, where its mouthful of teeth is ready to tear into its food.

FAST FACTS

LENGTH: up to 4.5 feet

DISTRIBUTION:
Northwest Pacific: Korea, Japan, and northern China

OCEAN DEPTHS: 1,200 feet

CHEW ON THIS!

The Japanese Sawshark has shown up on some menus in Japan as an ingredient in fishcakes.

IMPOSTER!
Don't be fooled! The sawfish looks a lot like a sawshark but they are actually in the ray family.

Technosharks

HOW DO YOU FOLLOW A SHARK? VERY CAREFULLY. THE TRUTH IS, THAT UNTIL THE LATE '90S, IT WAS NO EASY TASK FOR SCIENTISTS TO DISCOVER HOW SHARKS USE AND BEHAVE IN THEIR HABITATS.

Since then, thanks to innovations in technology, scientists have been busy collecting important data about these fascinating fish.

Shark tagging, a growing high-tech industry, involves capturing a shark, placing a nonrestrictive electronic "tag" on its fin, and then releasing the shark. The tag records data about where a shark goes, how deep down in the water the shark is, how much salt is in the water,

and more. The information stored in the tag is transmitted to a satellite and scientists can retrieve the data on their computers hundreds of miles away.

There are two basic kinds of tags. One kind transmits data to the satellite every time the shark surfaces, allowing scientists access to information in "real time." This kind of tag will obviously only work on sharks that usually swim near the surface. For sharks that swim deeper,

scientists often use a tag that records data and then pops up and off the shark at a predetermined time. Once the tag is bobbing on the surface of the water, it begins transmitting. Sometimes scientists will apply both kinds of tags to collect as much information as possible about a secretive swimmer.

SHARK BITE!

AN ELECTRIFYING WAY TO KEEP SHARKS SAFE

Sharks all too often wind up trapped in nets meant to catch tuna, and other fish. Now an electronic disk, no bigger than a half-dollar, can keep sharks safe. When attached to fishing gear and lowered into the water, the disk emits between 1.2 to 1.5 volts of electricity. A shark, able to sense much lower levels of electrical energy emitted by animals around it, is shocked (in a figurative sense only!) by the higher voltages and swims off in a hurry.

Attack Sharks

IN THE UNITED STATES, ON AVERAGE, LESS THAN ONE PERSON A YEAR DIES FROM A SHARK ATTACK.

And on average, in any given year, sharks attack only 33 people in the United States. So why has the public branded all sharks as being deadly killers?

Only a handful of shark species ever orders off the human side of the menu, and scientists suspect that a lot of the time it's because sharks think they're dining on a marine mammal or sea turtle. Once they get a taste of human, most sharks realize their mistake and swim off and look for dinner elsewhere.

According to one statistics professor, if you live in the United States, your odds of being attacked by a shark are a very comfy 1 in 9 million. Your odds of being attacked and *killed* by a shark are a seriously safe 1 in 400 million. It's a no-brainer that where the

Great White Shark

LENGTH: 12 TO 20 FEET
DISTRIBUTION: WORLDWIDE

WEIGHT: 2,500 TO 3,000 POUNDS

Sandtiger Shark

LENGTH: 4 TO 10 FEET **WEIGHT:** 200 TO 300 POUNDS
DISTRIBUTION: TROPICAL AND WARM WATERS; WORLDWIDE

Shortfin Mako

LENGTH: 6 TO 13 FEET **WEIGHT:** 135 TO 300 POUNDS
DISTRIBUTION: TROPICAL AND WARM WATERS, WORLDWIDE

Tiger Shark

LENGTH: 10 TO 18 FEET **WEIGHT:** 2,000 POUNDS
DISTRIBUTION: TROPICS AND SUBTROPICS

Bull Shark

LENGTH: 7 TO 10 FEET **WEIGHT:** 200 TO 400 POUNDS
DISTRIBUTION: FROM SOUTHERN BRAZIL TO NORTH CAROLINA AND
SOMETIMES UP TO NEW YORK; THE WEST INDIES; GULF OF MEXICO

Blue Shark

LENGTH: 6 TO 12.5 FEET **WEIGHT:** 260 TO 400 POUNDS
DISTRIBUTION: TROPICAL AND MILD WATERS; WORLDWIDE

Lemon Shark

LENGTH: 8 TO 10 FEET **WEIGHT:** 200 POUNDS
DISTRIBUTION: FROM BRAZIL TO NEW JERSEY;
FLORIDA'S WEST COAST TO TAMPA AND PENSACOLA

SHARK NOTE

The International Shark Attack File is the world's definitive source for compiling and keeping records of shark attacks. They have reports dating back to the mid-1500s!

sharks are, the risks are greatest. And since there are lots of sharks in Florida, it turns out that more than half of the attacks in any given year happen there. Your odds of being attacked in Florida are 1 in 430,000 and are 1 in 36 million of the attack being fatal.

That Really Bites

RESEARCHERS HAVE OBSERVED ENOUGH PATTERNS IN THE FEW SHARK ATTACKS THAT DO OCCUR EACH YEAR TO CLASSIFY THEM AS EITHER "PROVOKED" OR "UNPROVOKED" ATTACKS.

A provoked attack happens when a person is doing something to increase the interest of sharks in the area such as spearfishing or grabbing a shark. The shark may make an aggressive gesture to defend itself or its territory. If the person fails to recognize the gesture and doesn't back off, the shark may attack.

An unprovoked attack happens on an unsuspecting victim that is not doing anything that might attract sharks.

Researchers have divided unprovoked attacks into three major categories. The most common is the hit-and-run, which takes place in shallow water where people swim and surf. These attacks most likely happen when sharks mistake people for other foods, take one bite, and swim off with a bad taste in their mouths. Hit-and-run attacks are rarely fatal.

The bump-and-bite is a more serious kind of unprovoked attack. Sharks circle their victims, bump into them, and bite them—sometimes repeatedly. These attacks usually take place in deeper water than hit-and-run attacks.

A sneak attack, which also usually takes place in deeper water, may be the least common kind of unprovoked attack, but it is also the most deadly. The sneak attack is appropriately named, as it is when a shark attacks without warning, usually from below, and inflicts severe or fatal wounds.

SHARK NOTE

"Shark spotters" work on some beaches in South Africa. They scan the water searching for sharks and alert lifeguards when they spot one.

SHARK BITE!

TOP 10 UNUSUAL ITEMS SWALLOWED BY A SHARK

10. A leather wallet
9. A coil of copper wire
8. Packs of cigarettes
7. Cans of paint
6. Coats and other clothing
5. A license plate
4. An unopened can of sardines
3. A boat cushion
2. A Senegalese tom-tom drum
1. A tattooed human arm

Threatened Sharks

Top 5 Critically Endangered Sharks

1. Bizant River Shark
2. Dumb Gulper Shark
3. Ganges Shark
4. New Guinea River Shark
5. Pondicherry Shark

ONE THIRD OF ALL SHARK SPECIES ARE NOW THREATENED WITH EXTINCTION.

What exactly does that mean? A threatened species is one that is vulnerable to extinction in the near future.

What's going on? What could possibly be posing a threat to so many sharks? The answer is simple: it's people. It turns out that not only do people have overactive imaginations about how deadly sharks really are, but they also have a strong appetite for the fish themselves. That's right, people around the planet like the taste of shark meat so much that it has resulted in severe overfishing of many species. And overfishing has been cited as a major reason for the decline of numerous shark populations.

In some places, shark fins are considered such a delicacy that sharks are captured, "de-finned," and

Hammerhead Shark

Basking Shark

Great White Shark

Whale Shark

thrown back in the water. This is a path to certain death, since no fish can survive without its fins.

An alarming number of sharks also perish each year as "**bycatch**"—they get caught in nets set up by commercial fishermen trawling for tuna and swordfish.

Sharks are species that have slow reproduction rates, which means that when their numbers plummet due to overfishing

or for any other reason, their overall population is slow to recover. Unless fishing is properly managed, the numbers of any species can dip dramatically.

Sharks can become threatened from loss of habitat or from pollution, but the most common reason is from over fishing.

Blue Shark

SHARK BITE!

MEGAMOUTH 41

In 2009, Megamouth 41 – so named because it was the 41st of the extremely rare species to be reported – died after becoming tangled in a fishing net in the Philippines. A local field scientist identified the 1,100-pound, 13-foot-long fish before the fishermen decided to cook it in coconut milk and serve up a feast.

What do you think? Since the fish was already dead was it okay to eat it? Or should scientists have been allowed to study Megamouth 41 in the hopes that they could learn more about this rare species?

SHARK NOTE

Close to 11 million blue sharks are killed annually for their fins.

Swellshark
Cephaloscyllium ventriosum

THE STOUT-BODIED, FLAT-HEADED SWELLSHARK GETS ITS NAME FROM ITS ABILITY TO BLOW ITSELF UP LIKE A BALLOON TO BE TWICE ITS SIZE! NOW, THAT REALLY *IS* ONE SWELL SHARK!

Why does the Swellshark do this very cool thing? It's sort of the same idea as when a frightened cat puffs itself up to look bigger to a would-be attacker. The swellshark, in doubling its size by taking water into its stomach, is trying to make itself too big for larger sharks and seals to sink their teeth into.

FAST FACTS

LENGTH: up to 39 inches
DISTRIBUTION: subtropical eastern Pacific
OCEAN DEPTHS: 1,500 feet

This nocturnal shark spends its days hiding in caves and rock crevices to stay safe, and if it feels threatened it will bend its body into a U-shape, grab its tail with its mouth, and begin to suck in water. Its body balloons out until the shark is wedged tightly inside its hiding place and cannot be easily dislodged by a hungry predator.

As for its own hunting style, the Swellshark stays on the sea bottom, where its markings allow it to blend in with its surroundings. It waits for prey to swim by and will either pounce or just sit there and open its mouth for customers!

CHEW ON THIS!

When the Swellshark is full of water, it really *is* like a balloon. It rises in the water, and can make the shark look too big for a would-be predator to eat.

Goblin Shark

Mitsukurina owstoni

NO, THIS SHARK IS NOT WEARING A HALLOWEEN COSTUME; IT REALLY LOOKS LIKE THAT.

The Goblin Shark has a pinkish, soft, flabby body and bluish fins. But it's the head that really generates the most attention for this bottom dweller rarely seen near the water's surface.

The shark has a pointed, beaklike snout protruding from a long head that contains tiny eyes and a large jaw with slender and narrow teeth. Is it a face only Mother Nature can love? Well, it's a head and face where everything has its function.

Because the shark lives so deep in the sea, very little sunlight penetrates way down there, which means this shark doesn't rely on sight as much as other senses to find a meal. Thus the tiny eyes. The snout is covered with receptors that help the shark locate prey, some of it hiding in the muddy ocean bottom. The snout can serve double duty as a shovel. The Goblin Shark's teeth are perfectly suited for its diet of bony fish, shrimps, octopus, and squid. So the Goblin Shark may not be decorative, but it sure is functional!

CHEW ON THIS!

The Goblin Shark has 50 needlelike teeth in the first row of several rows of teeth: 26 in the upper jaw and 24 in the lower jaw. Its back teeth are specialized for crushing things like crabs, which scientists also think it eats.

FAST FACTS

LENGTH: up to 12.6 feet

WEIGHT: up to 460 pounds

DISTRIBUTION: Portugal, Japan, India, and Australia

OCEAN DEPTHS: 4,265 feet

Thresher Shark
Alopias vulpinus

THIS SHARK LIKES TO STIR THINGS UP—LITERALLY!

The Thresher Shark puts its distinctive tail to use by using it to stir the waters around schooling fish, creating a mini whirlpool. The fish huddle tightly together, thinking that's the best way for them to protect themselves. This is exactly what the Thresher Shark wants. When mackerel, menhaden, herring, and other schooling fish are swimming very close together, each mouthful the shark takes in is packed with extra protein!

The Thresher Shark's tail can account for up to one-third of the fish's entire body

weight, so it packs a powerful punch. The Thresher Shark has to do a lot of work because it has relatively weak jaws and teeth. That's why it swims quickly into the whirling mass of fish with its mouth wide open.

When the Thresher Shark is in the process of herding together a meal, that's when it's most likely to be seen near the shore. The shark can swim at high speeds for short bursts and can even leap out of the water. It's an impressive sight, but no one is totally sure why the Thresher Shark does it.

FAST FACTS

LENGTH: greater than 16 feet
WEIGHT: up to 750 pounds
DISTRIBUTION:
Tropical and cold-temperate oceans worldwide
OCEAN DEPTHS: 1,800 feet

CHEW ON THIS!

The Thresher Shark is classified as a game fish in the United States and South Africa, and is hunted for sport in both countries. In addition, the shark's skin is used for leather, its liver's oil is used in vitamins, and its meat and fins also have commercial value.

Simply Sharktastic

FASCINATING FACTS ABOUT THESE FABULOUS FISH CAN FILL ALL THE OCEANS OF THE WORLD! HERE ARE JUST A FEW TO CHEW ON!

A SHARK IS NOT JUST ANY BODY

1. Some species of shark throw up by forcing their stomachs through their mouths so they can empty them out!

2. Some sharks close their eyes when they bite their prey! And some sharks have a **nictitating membrane** that slides over their eyes to protect them from fish that fight back or from flying flesh.

3. A shark's tongue, called a **basihyal**, doesn't move and isn't even where a shark's taste buds are!

4. A shark's skin feels like sandpaper, thanks to its large scales.

5. The Silky Shark got its name because its scales are so small its skin feels smooth.

6. A shark's belly is lighter in color than its back. This "**countershading**" helps a shark blend into the water when seen from above or below.

FOOD FOR THOUGHT

1. Some sharks eat so much at one time that they don't have to eat again for a month!

2. Sharks don't chew their food, they just swallow whole mouthfuls.

3. Most sharks only eat live food, but tiger sharks will also eat the rotting flesh of dead animals.

4. A shark eats up to 10% of its body weight a week.

OH, MY WORD!

1. Sharks, skates, and rays are not only all related, but because they have cartilage instead of bones they are called **elasmobranch** fish.

2. Have a real fear of sharks? Then you suffer from **selachophobia**.

FEARLESS FREELOADERS

1. Remora fish are called "sharksuckers." Thanks to a sucking disc on the top of their heads, they spend their lives clinging to sharks. They eat the sharks' leftover scraps and save energy by letting the sharks do the swimming!

2. Some small fishes are dental hygenists—they go into sharks' mouths and dine off the bits of food they clean out from between sharks' teeth!

UNDER ATTACK!

1. You have more chance of being struck by lightning than you do of being attacked by a shark.

2. More people die from bee stings than from shark bites every year.

3. The book, *Jaws* by Peter Benchley is based on real shark attacks that took place in New Jersey back in 1916, when four people died in 12 days.

OH, BABY!

1. Many shark pups grow as eggs that hatch inside their mothers before they hit the ocean water fully formed.

2. Some shark pups can't wait to be birthed to become predators—they eat their siblings while they're all still inside Mom!

3. It is possible for a female shark to have up to 100 shark pups at a time.

4. A shark mom doesn't take care of her babies. As soon as they're born, they're on their own.

5. Some female sharks give birth once every two years.

Epaulette Shark

Hemiscyllium

THIS SMALL NOCTURNAL SHARK HANGS OUT NEAR THE BOTTOM OF THE SHALLOW WATERS OF THE CORAL REEFS OR TIDAL POOLS IT SWIMS IN.

Actually, if you watch an Epaulette shark move, you might say it looks more like it's walking than swimming. This shark wriggles its body and uses its paddle-shape pectoral fins to push itself forward over rocky surfaces.

The Epaulette Shark belongs to a group of sharks called carpet sharks. Since many of them hug the ocean floor, you might think that's why they are named for floor coverings. But they apparently are so named because of the speckled, ruglike patterns on their skin.

The Epaulette Shark in particular is known and named for its enormous "eye spots" located above each pectoral fin. Scientists think the eye spots scare off would-be predators (which include other kinds of sharks), fooling them into thinking it must be a bigger fish than it really is, based on the size of its eyes!

FAST FACTS

LENGTH: up to 3.5 feet
DISTRIBUTION:
Australia and New Zealand
OCEAN DEPTHS: 160 feet

CHEW ON THIS!

Scientists have discovered that the Epaulette Shark can survive in water with low levels of oxygen for several hours without suffering any ill effects. It just switches off any nonessential body functions during that time!

Whale Shark
Rhincodon typus

THE WHALE SHARK IS THE WORLD'S UNDISPUTED LARGEST FISH.

The longest one measures an impressive 65 feet long, which is longer than 10 full-grown men are tall. But it's hard to know how much this giant weighs, since there's no scale big enough to hold one! Scientists have used mathematical calculations to arrive at a probable weight.

You might think a shark this big, with a mouth so huge, eats lots of large marine creatures. But when the whale shark goes in search of food, it mostly eats tiny plankton or small schooling fishes.

The Whale Shark has 3000 tiny teeth in

CHEW ON THIS!

Scientists have been able to weigh some body parts of dead Whale Sharks. One had a heart that weighed 43 pounds! Another had a 900-pound liver!

its mouth, but scientists don't think it use its teeth when it eats. The shark simply opens its mouth wide and sweeps in food through filter feeders. The Whale Shark swims through the water, bobbing its head back and forth to catch everything in its path—which can also include things it doesn't want to eat and which it will throw up later! Or the Whale Shark will shoot upward through schools of fish with its mouth open, which is a more active, aggressive feeding style.

FAST FACTS

LENGTH: up to 45 feet

WEIGHT: estimated to be more than 13 tons (26,000 pounds)

DISTRIBUTION: All warm temperate and tropical seas, except the Mediterranean

OCEAN DEPTHS: 2,296 feet

Frilled Shark
Chlamydoselachus anguineus

YOU MAY THINK YOU'RE LOOKING AT A SEA SERPENT OR SOME KIND OF SEA MONSTER WHEN YOU FIRST LOOK AT THE FRILLED SHARK (SOMETIMES CALLED FRILL SHARK).

But you're looking at a near-threatened, primitive shark species that scientists believe has changed very little over millions of years.

The shark's serpentlike appearance is due in part to its long, thin shape. And the dorsal fin, usually pointy and prominent on a shark's back, is small and located near the Frilled Shark's tail.

Then there's the serpent-shape head that looks like it's all mouth, thanks to the jaw extending all the way to the back of the shark's head. Add in what looks like a frilled collar around the throat where the gill openings begin, and you're looking at one really unique fish!

The Frilled Shark is even more impressive when it opens its mouth to reveal 300 forklike teeth, tightly packed into its jaw. It needs these grippers to hold onto the smooth skin of its preferred prey: squid, cuttlefish, and octopus.

FAST FACTS

LENGTH: up to 6 feet 4 inches

DISTRIBUTION: scattered locations in the Atlantic and Pacific Oceans

OCEAN DEPTHS: between 160 and 660 feet

CHEW ON THIS!

Scientists believe the Frilled Shark may have the longest gestation period on record. Research remains underway, but it looks like the Frilled Shark is pregnant for about 3½ years!

Pacific Angelshark

Squatina californica

AT FIRST GLANCE, THIS SHARK MORE CLOSELY RESEMBLES A RAY (A SHARK RELATIVE), THAN AN ACTUAL SHARK.

This is in large part due to the Pacific Angelshark's flat, broad body and large pectoral fins. When viewed from above, the shark's body shape resembles an angel, hence its name.

This nocturnal shark spends the day snoozing on the sea floor where it blends into its surroundings and only its eyes

FAST FACTS

LENGTH: up to 5 feet

WEIGHT: up to 176 pounds

DISTRIBUTION: Temperate and tropical waters worldwide

OCEAN DEPTHS: 492 feet or deeper

stick up out of the mud or sand. At night it swims near the ocean floor, hunting a variety of bony fishes and other food.

The Pacific Angelshark is itself a food fish. The shark also winds up as bycatch and is hurt or killed when it gets tangled in fishing nets and lines.

IMPOSTER!
Don't be fooled! The Guitarfish looks a lot like a Pacific Angelshark but they are actually in the ray family.

Are You Shark Bait? QUIZ

THINK YOU KNOW A THING OR TWENTY ABOUT
SHARKS? TRY TESTING YOUR KNOWLEDGE BELOW.
ALL THE INFORMATION YOU NEED IS LURKING
SOMEWHERE IN THE PAGES OF THIS BOOK.

1. *Helicoprion* was:
A) a prehistoric helicopter
B) a shark from 250 million years ago
C) a dinosaur

2. *Megaladon's* teeth were:
A) very yellow
B) wooden
C) up to 6.5 inches long

3. Sharks are related to:
A) skates and rays
B) lawyers
C) whales

4. A shark's skeleton is made up of:
A) plankton
B) cartilage
C) bones

5. Denticles are:
A) baby shark teeth
B) scales on the shark's skin
C) teeth shaped like icicles

6. A shark's vision is best:
A) from a distance
B) close up
C) when it's looking right at you!

7. Sharks breathe with:
A) gills
B) lungs
C) they don't need to breath underwater

8. Sharks can hear:
A) the music from *Jaws*
B) seagulls flapping in the air
C) low-pitched sounds

9. A shark's lateral line:
A) divides the fish in half
B) helps it sense vibrations
C) keeps it balanced

10. The ampullae of Lorenzini are:
A) scent receptors
B) electrical energy receptors
C) Italian sharks

11. The whale shark is:
A) a cross between a whale and a shark
B) the biggest shark
C) a shark that swims with whales

12. Each year, this many people in the
U.S. die from a shark attack:
A) less than one
B) 37.5
C) more than are struck by lightning

13. Shark tagging is:
A) a way to get info on how sharks live
B) very dangerous when it's the shark's
turn to find you
C) a way to catalog all the sharks in the ocean

14. **This many sharks are in danger of becoming extinct:**
A) at least one-third
B) are you kidding—they're big predators
C) only a few

15. **When a shark loses a tooth:**
A) it grows a new one
B) it can't eat
C) it puts it under a rock for the tooth fishy

16. **A "provoked" shark attack happens:**
A) when you call the shark names
B) never
C) when you're doing something that attracts sharks, such as spearfishing

17. **People fish for sharks because:**
A) people eat them
B) people want to put sharks in their fish tanks
C) sharks eat too many fish people want to eat

18. **The pectoral fins are:**
A) what a shark flexes to show its muscles
B) what gives a shark lift in the water
C) just decorative, not functional

19. **Sharks often attack people:**
A) by mistake
B) when they want a little bite of something
C) because they like how people taste

20. **A hit-and-run shark attack most often occurs:**
A) on local streets
B) when you're not doing anything that attracts the interest of sharks
C) at the bottom of the ocean

TURN TO PAGE 48 FOR THE ANSWERS.

SCORE KEY

0–5 CORRECT
You're in deep, shark-infested waters

6–10 CORRECT
Check yourself for cuts; now is not the time for a shark to smell you

11–17 CORRECT
you're swimming in safe water

18–20 CORRECT
fintastic!

Glossary

AMPULLAE OF LORENZINI: Receptor cells in a shark's head that allows the shark to pick up low levels of electric energy emitted by other animals

ANAL FIN: Many sharks have two of these fins that help stabilize them in the water

BARBELS: Feelers on the sides of the snouts of some sharks, like the Japanese Sawshark, that help them detect prey

BASIHYAL: A shark's tongue; it has no tastebuds and doesn't move in the mouth

BYCATCH: Term for a shark or other fish that gets caught in a commercial fishing net meant for other fish

CARNIVORE: An animal that eats other animals

CARTILAGE: A tough but flexible material like in human ears that makes up a shark's skeleton

CAUDAL FIN: Another name for a shark's tail fin

COUNTERSHADING: The way a shark's light belly and dark back help it blend into the water when it is seen from either above or below

CRUSTACEAN: Aquatic animals with hard protective shells and antennae, like crabs and lobsters

DERMAL DENTICLES: Tooth-like scales on a shark's skin

DORSAL FIN: The fin on a shark's back that helps stabilize it as it moves through the water

ELASMOBRANCH: What fish with cartilage instead of bones are called

FOSSIL: Remains from ancient animals

GILL PUMP: Muscles that suck in water and push it past a shark's gills

INFRASOUNDS: Low-pitched sounds that sharks can hear in the water

LATERAL LINE: A sensory organ for feeling the vibrations of other animals in the water

NICTITATING MEMBRANE: Also called the third eyelid, a thin protective covering for a shark's eyes

PECTORAL FINS: Fins located on either side of a shark's body for moving up and down

PELVIC FINS: Fins that help keep a shark balanced

PLANKTON: Extremely tiny living organisms eaten by other animals, like whale sharks

RAM VENTILATION: The way most sharks get oxygen from the water, whereby water passes over the gills as the sharks move forward

SELACHOPHOBIA: An extreme fear of sharks

SERRATED: With notches, like a saw

ANSWER KEY TO QUIZ ON PAGE 46

1: B 2: C 3: A 4: B 5: B 6: A 7: A
8: C 9: B 10: B 11: B 12: A 13: A 14: A
15: A 16: C 17: A 18: B 19: A 20: B